Printed and Published in Great Britain by D.C. THOMSON & CO., LTD., 185 Fleet Street, London, EC4A 2HS.
© D.C. THOMSON & CO., LTD., 1991 ISBN 0-85116-519-2

Suddenly— WE HAVE A NEW PUPIL, CHILDREN—MEET TREVOR.

MY FRIENDS CALL ME "CLEVER TREVOR"!

OPEN YOUR SUM BOOKS AT PAGE 94.

HUH! THESE SUM BOOKS ARE FOR KIDS! DON'T YOU USE THE "ADVANCED EXTREMELY DIFFICULT SUMS" BOOKS?

FOR THIS THICK LOT? CHUCKLE! OF COURSE NOT! I USE THE ADVANCED BOOKS TO STUDY AT HOME, DO YOU?

ME? OH, NO— I WRITE THEM!

GULP!

MIFFED →

GASP! HE'S SO CLEVER HE CAN WORK OUT HOW TO HIT THE BALL PERFECTLY! AWE!

DONK!

ERK!

Back in class— JUST A MINUTE, TEACHER—THAT'S NOT QUITE CORRECT.

$$\frac{A}{B} \times Y = Z$$

EH?

HE THINKS HE KNOWS MORE THAN ME—AND HE DOES! MOAN!

$$\frac{A}{B} \times Y = W \qquad W = \frac{RS}{TU} \times Y$$

$$Y = \frac{10036}{26\ldots}$$

YOU'RE ONE OF US NOW, TEACHER!

PHEW! TIME TO GO HOME AT LAST! THAT WAS TOO MUCH FOR ME!

AND ME! GASP!

FAN

DEPRESSED

I DON'T THINK HE'S SO CLEVER— I'LL TEST HIM OUT.

I'D LIKE TO ASK YOU SOME QUESTIONS.

FIRE AWAY, DEAR BOY.

TAP! TAP!

TOLD YOU HE WASN'T SO CLEVER—HE DIDN'T ANSWER ONE QUESTION!

HAPPY AGAIN →

WELL DONE, SMIFFY —YOU'VE GOT RID OF THAT RIVAL!

BASH ST. SCHOOL

R-I-P!

JERK

JUDDER

WH- WHERE AM I? WHO AM I?

Cuthbert's house— I'M SO GRATEFUL TO YOU, SMIFFY! YOU DO ASK SOME FASCINATING QUESTIONS!

SLURP! DO I? SLOO!

GOLD-PLATED

PURRR!

COO! LOOK AT THE HEAD'S NEW CAR!

WHAT A BEAUTY!

OO! SHOW US YOUR NEW CAR, HEAD! PLEASE! PLEASE!

WISH I HAD A CAR LIKE HEAD'S!

FIRST, YOU'LL NOTICE THE SLEEK DESIGN.

WE'VE ALWAYS FANCIED PLAYING UNDER FLOODLIGHTS!

But—

AW! IT'S STUCK!

HEH-HEH! THAT WILL STOP THEIR GAME!

DOINK!

HOW DOES THE AERIAL WORK?

GLUM

WHAT A SUPER NUT-CRACKER!

CRACK! WHIRRR!

OOF!

PING!

FASTEN YOUR SEAT-BELTS!

IT HAS A RECORDED VOICE WHICH TELLS YOU WHAT TO DO.

GIVE THE PUPILS THE AFTERNOON OFF!

EH?

GROAN! THIS NEW CAR'S GOING TO BE NOTHING BUT BOTHER WITH THOSE KIDS AROUND.

WISH I HAD A CAR LIKE YOURS, TEACHER!

PROUD

COMPLETELY IGNORING TEACHER'S CAR

PHEW!

Headed Off

THIS IS THOMAS TRAYNOR—HE'S NEW TO THE SCHOOL.

SIT DOWN AND OPEN YOUR BOOKS, MY LAD.

SWIVEL

PUSH

SPLAT!

BRAVO! BRIGHT CHAP!

WHAT'S 74 MINUS 27?

YAWN! DON'T KNOW AND DON'T CARE.

IF LIVERPOOL HAVE SCORED 74 GOALS AND LOST 27, WHAT'S THEIR GOAL DIFFERENCE?

So—

TRA-LAA!

GASP! WHEEZE! MY OLD LUNGS HAVE HAD ENOUGH!

Later—

GASP! PUFF! WHEEZE!

FRESH AS A DAISY!

HE CERTAINLY PUTS TEACHER IN THE SHADE.

HMM! WONDER IF I COULD GET THOMAS AS A REPLACEMENT FOR TEACHER?

WHAT? CAN'T HAVE THIS!

HMM! ONLY ONE CHAIR.

HEAD'S STUDY

GROVEL HERE

Meanwhile—

THAT STUDENT TEACHER'S GREAT! HE'LL BE A HEADMASTER IN NO TIME!

GULP! I DON'T WANT TO BE OUT OF A JOB!

PAPER CAPER

We're good at fetching newspapers for our masters.

DIM DOG

Bet your dog's bitten a hole in yours!

DIM BOY

Yes ~ but that's OK...

Daft dog!

...When you've a hole in your paper...

...you can see where you're going!

Oh, no! My football team lost 5 ~ 0!

The result's not in my paper ~ that bit's been eaten!

I'm going to get you a reward for biting my paper.

I'm worried ~ those two aren't as daft as they should be!

SWEET SHOP

CONFECION

There ~ eat that.

Ha-ha! Needn't have bothered ~ they ARE dim!

It's a toffee newspaper ~ the latest treat for dogs!

SPACE CASE

The Kids are playing rounders—

WAP!

But...

URK!

SPLUDGE!

TOPPLE

CLASS IIB

PIFFLE AND POPPYCOCK, SILLY BOY!

CLASS IIB

LOOK!

GASP! IT IS A MARTIAN!

GUBBLE-WARFLE-SPLURT!

WHAT'S HE SAYING?

AH! HE'S GOT THE HANG OF IT!

CHOMP! CHOMP!

PICKLE BARREL

WHERE'S YOUR SPACE-SHIP?

WOW! MUST BE LIKE DOCTOR WHO'S "TARDIS"!

G-GULP! D-DON'T BE T-TOO HASTY!

A TOY

Meanwhile, up above—

TIME FOR OUR YEARLY BATH, LADS.

BASH ST. BIRDS

SPLASH!

SPLOOSH!

TEN LITTLE BASH STREET FROGS

Ten Little Bash Street Frogs
Sat on a speckled log
Eating some most delicious flies (Yum-Yum).
One with a joyful croak,
Just for a little joke —
Elbowed his neighbour in the pond.

Nine Little Bash Street Frogs
Sat on a speckled log
Eating some most delicious flies (Yum-Yum).
One, rather poor of sight,
Went for a hop one night —
Leapt by mistake into the pond.

Eight Little Bash Street Frogs
Sat on a speckled log
Eating some most delicious flies (Yum-Yum).
One who was rather dim,
Saw someone just like him —
Joined his reflection in the pond.

Seven Little Bash Street Frogs
Sat on a speckled log
Eating some most delicious flies (Yum-Yum).
One, he ate so much food,
He went right through the wood —
Caused a big splash in Bash Street pond.

Six Little Bash Street Frogs
Sat on a speckled log
Eating some most delicious flies (Yum-Yum).
One rather hairy chap,
Felt like a little nap —
DROPPED OFF and landed in the pond.

FUN and GAMES

MMM! I LOVE LEMON DROPS!

YAROOP!

Soon—

TIME I WASHED THE WINDOWS.

GOAL!

THUMP!

SWOOSH!

SPLUTTER!

KITCHEN

THIS IS FOR THE HEAD'S LUNCH.

OLIVE—SCHOOL COOK →

BOUNCE

GLURGH!

BONK!

BOUNCE

GAH! THE KIDS HAVE MADE ME EAT THIS GHASTLY STUFF.

Later—

WONDER IF IT'S SAFE TO CROSS THAT PLAYGROUND NOW?

EXIT   EXIT

IT IS SAFE—THEY'RE NOT PLAYING ANY GAMES.

PART 2
TEACHER
COME
HOME

POST!

IT'S A POSTCARD FROM TEACHER ON SAFARI IN AFRICA!

HOWDY, PARTNERS—I'M YOUR NEW TEACHER—HOMER, SHERIFF OF TOMBSTONE GULCH!

OO! I'VE ALWAYS WANTED TO MEET A FILM STAR!

IDIOT! HOMER THE SHERIFF, NOT OMAR SHARIF!

WOWEE! WHAT A GRIZZLY LOOKING HOMBRE!

Then—

BRING THE GEAR IN HERE, DEPUTIES!

Soon—

A FINE JAIL FOR KEEPING LAWBREAKERS IN!

Then—

WHAT'S THAT?

SLURP!

RUSTLE! RUSTLE!

Eventually—

HE'S GOT TO GO!

At lunchtime—

OUR NEW TEACHER IS DOING A WONDERFUL JOB, YOUR LADYSHIP.

BASH STREET SCHOOL

SCHOOL GOVERNESS

LOOK, TEACHER!

INDIANS!

LOOKS LIKE HE WON'T BE BACK FOR A WHILE. WONDER WHO OUR NEW TEACHER WILL BE?

HAVING A WONDERFUL TIME — GLAD YOU'RE NOT HERE *Teacher*

BASH STREET SCHOOL, GREAT BRITAIN.

Then— *TRING!*

YAH! WE'RE NOT GOING IN YET—WE'RE ENJOYING OUR GAME!

Suddenly—

I RECKON MY SPARE STETSON IS NEEDED HERE!

In class—

QUIET DOWN THERE, GIRL!

YAK- YAK- YAK YAK- YAK!

YAK- YAK- GLUB!

POP GUN

FANCY SHOOTING, EH?

RUSTLERS GO TO JAIL!

ERK!

WHAT'S GOING ON?

GUNFIGHTERS GO TO JAIL, TOO!

TAKE THAT, YOU VARMINT—OH, GEE!

WH- WHAT?

POP!

The Head is not amused!

SPLUTTER! FUME!

RED WITH ANGER

GET OUT, YOU UNSPEAKABLE OAF!

I'M MOVING OUT!

HAR- HAR! LOOKS LIKE THAT COWBOY'S NO MATCH FOR A REDSKIN ON THE WARPATH!

PART 3

TEACHER COME HOME

I CAN'T GET ANYONE TO TAKE OVER FROM TEACHER WHILE HE'S ON HOLIDAY, HUNTING LIONS IN AFRICA.

AH, WINSTON! THE VERY CAT!

HISS!

YEEOW!

BOOMF!

SPLAT!

THIS IS ANOTHE THING WE CATS D

WHAT'S GOT INTO THE KIDS?

SAFEST PLACE TO BE!

FOLLOW ON, KIDS!

STOP THAT DIN!

GET OUT OF IT!

WE'VE HAD NOTHING BUT BOTHER SINCE WINSTON BECAME OUR TEACHER!

Next day—

WHAT'S THAT FUNNY PONG?

TRADING FACES

PART 4

TEACHER COME HOME

The Bash Street Teacher is on Safari in Africa—

THIS IS FUN COMPARED WITH TEACHING CLASS II B. WONDER IF HEAD'S GOT A RELIEF TEACHER TO REPLACE ME YET?

He hasn't!

WHO CAN I FIND DAFT ENOUGH TO TEACH CLASS II B?

'MORNING! WHAT ARE YOU GOING TO TEACH ME TODAY?

EH?

SCREECH OF HOOVES!

NO! NO! YOU'RE THE TEACHER— YOU SIT HERE.

RIGHT! WHEN DID NELSON FIGHT THE BATTLE OF BANNOCKBURN?

ER—BUT—EM—

But—

CLASS II B

FLOUR

SPLUTTER! OH, NO! HE'S GOT IT WRONG—IT'S THE PUPILS WHO PLAY TRICKS ON THE TEACHER, NOT THE OTHER WAY ROUND!

HAR—HAR—HAR!

GET YOUR BOOKS OUT, CHILDREN!

OOYAH!

OUCH!

SPLAT!

TEE—HEE!

BAH! WHAT DO THOSE NOISY URCHINS WANT?

CLASS II B

HEAD! HEAD!

HEAD IS DAFT

WH- WHAT?

HOW DARE YOU! WHAT A DREADFUL INFLUENCE ON THESE POOR, DEAR CHILDREN!

Then—

COOEE! I'VE JUST POPPED ROUND TO CONGRATULATE YOU ON MY SON'S EXCELLENT MARKS.

SMIFFY'S DAD

THE VERY MAN—HE'S AS DAFT AS A BRUSH!

I WAS WONDERING IF YOU COULD HELP ME OUT...

Next morning—

WONDER WHAT YOUR DAD WILL BE LIKE AS A TEACHER?

BRILLIANT, NO DOUBT!

JUST AFTER BREAKFAST!

EXCELLENT! GO TO THE TOP OF THE CLASS!

That evening—

WHY AREN'T YOU DOING YOUR HOMEWORK, DANNY?

BUT WE ARE DOING THE HOMEWORK SMIFFY'S DAD GAVE US.

GASP!

HOMEWORK
2 HOURS EXTRA FOOTBALL

Next day—

IT'S GREAT HAVING SMIFFY'S DAD AS TEACHER!

OF!

QUIET IN CLASS!

YAOO!

WHIMPER!

OO!

SUPER CANE THIS HO-HO!

BAH! WE'VE HAD ENOUGH OF THIS.

PRESS

THAT'S ANOTHER TEACHER OUT OF THE WAY.

INNOCENCE

At Smiffy's house—

HOW DID SCHOOL GO TODAY?

SUPER! DAD GOT EXPELLED!

POLISH

WELL DONE—HAVE AN EXTRA HELPING OF FISH AND CUSTARD FOR DOING SO WELL.

YUMMY! MY FAVOURITE!

SARDINES AND SAGO

PRUNES AND MINCE

WHAT A FAMILY!

EDITOR'S VOICE

PART 5
TEACHER COME HOME

WHO CAN I GET TO TEACH THE LITTLE ANIMALS OF CLASS IIB WHILE TEACHER'S IN AFRICA?

I'M AN EXPERT WITH ANIMALS—AND I'VE ALWAYS WANTED TO BE A TEACHER!

OOYAH! NASTY SHEEPDOG!

ZIP!

HAR-HAR! I'M FARMER INNES DEN, YOUR NEW TEACHER!

COME WITH ME—! I'M GOING TO GIVE YOU LINES FOR TRYING TO SKIP SCHOOL!

So—

WHERE ARE WE GOING?

Suddenly—

OOYAH!

S-PRANG

AHA!

OH-OH! LOOKS LIKE DANNY'S FOUND A NEEDLE IN A HAYSTACK!

Back in school—

THAT WRITING'S A DISGRACE!

Then—

WHERE IS THA FARMER?

CLUC CLUC

SNORT! GRUNT! OINK!

STOP THESE PIGGISH NOISES, FAT BOY!

Then—

ERK! I'VE FORGOTTEN IT'S THE ANIMALS' FEEDING TIME!

NEIGH!

CLUCK!

BAA!

QUACK!

MOO!

WONDER HOW THE NEW TEACHER'S GETTING ON?

CLASS IIB

HOT AIR BUFFOON!

"**WHAT-HO, chaps!**" said Wing Commander Gander, fiddling with his moustache (he also played piano with his ears — but only on special occasions).

"Splendid day for a balloon ride!" He opened the gate for the Kids and Teacher to come through. Teacher stumbled towards him (Danny had tied his laces together).

"I understand you're considered an expert in this field," said Teacher, picking himself up.

"I'm considered an expert wherever I go!" retorted the Commander, drawing himself to his full height. Once he finished sketching he crossed the field and clambered into his balloon. "Would you like to join me in the basket?" he asked.

"We'd rather join Fatty in his picnic basket!" exclaimed Spotty as he and the others tucked into the huge snack Fatty had brought with him. Fatty's anger boiled over but before he could do anything his soup boiled over too, scalding Teacher's leg. Teacher hopped around in agony. "I've reached my breaking point!" he snapped. "Get into that balloon this instant!" Teacher herded the kids into the basket before hopping in to join them on his one good leg.

"Take us up, Commander!" said Teacher, one leg dangling in the breeze to cool.

"Chocks away!" shouted the Commander, taking a bag of chocolate buttons from a surprised Fatty and throwing them over the side. The balloon didn't move.

"Er . . . shouldn't you fire the burners?" said Cuthbert in a small voice.

"Good idea!" replied the Commander in a large voice. "You're fired!" he bellowed and threw the burners over the side as well.

"Just as well I had a curry for breakfast!" said Fatty, before burping noisily into the balloon above his head. His fiery breath filled the balloon and it rose gracefully into the air.

The kids looked down at the splendid views beneath them. "I can see a flock of sheep!" said 'Erbert excitedly as they continued to rise. "Those are clouds, short-sighted youth!" said Teacher in a raised voice (he was standing on tip-toe).

Soon they were floating very high up indeed. "It's getting quite cold up here," said Teacher icily.

"Yes, there's a nip in the air," agreed Sidney, pinching Teacher to prevent frostbite. Teacher's face took on a set expression — his teeth had frozen together.

Just then a large bird with an even larger beak flew into view. It was heading straight for the balloon! "I'll shoo it away!" said the Commander, removing a shoe and throwing it at the bird. He missed. "I'll sock it on the beak!" he continued, removing a sock and throwing it, too, at the unfortunate bird. He missed again.

Before the idiotic aviator could remove any more clothing the bird caught sight of Plug's foul features and, in a terrified flurry of feathers, it migrated North instead of South. "Squawerk!"

A loose feather drifted down and lodged in the Commander's moustache. He let out a mighty sneeze and his teeth shot out, embedding themselves in the side of the balloon. "You idiot!" hissed Teacher, in time with the punctured balloon. "Hand out the parachutes before we all crash!" The Commander looked sheepish. "I forgot to bring any!" he bleated.

The balloon had picked up speed as it zoomed crazily earthwards. The wind whined in the kids' ears and Teacher and Cuthbert whined in each other's ears. "Help! Mummy!" they squealed.

As they sped towards the ground Danny noticed a strange sight. "That haystack's moving!" he said. Sure enough, a haystack did appear to be following them — it was Smiffy pushing a barrowload of straw! FLUMP! The balloon basket landed softly in the hay. "Well done, Smiffy!" cheered the kids, safely on the ground once more.

"Wait a minute!" said Teacher sharply (he'd found the needle in the haystack with the seat of his trousers), "Why weren't you here in time to go up with us?"

"The Commander is my crazy uncle," explained Smiffy. "I knew something would go wrong!"

The kids carried Smiffy shoulder high, "Good old Smiffy! He may be daft but he's definitely not stupid!"

The POTION COMMOTION

I'VE GOT A HEADACHE!

I'VE GOT TOOTHACHE!

MY NOSE IS BLOCKED!

I'LL INVITE MY GRANNY ROUND TO HELP YOU—SHE'S GOT HERBAL REMEDIES FOR ALMOST EVERYTHING.

Five minutes later—

NOW TO WIPE OFF THE OINTMENT.

WIPE

RUB

HUH! IT HASN'T REMOVED MY SPOTS!

HMM!

MIRROR

IT'S DONE A GREAT JOB ON YOUR HANKY THOUGH, HASN'T IT?

OOYAH!

WHERE AM I?

CRUNCH!

THAT STUFF'S MADE 'ERBERT'S EYESIGHT WORSE!

OO! OW! YOW!

DON'T WORRY—I'VE GOT TOE TONIC.

SORE

THIS SHOULD DO IT.

SPLUTCH!

REALLY? PERHAPS YOU COULD CURE MY SORE BACK.

Enter Olive—

TEA'S UP—WOOPS!

AWFUL COOK

BUMP!

YEROO

SPLOOSH!

CLICK!

TOP THAT!

BRILLIANT TRAIN, SIDNEY.

CHUG-A-CHUG!

CUTHBERT CRINGEWORTHY, CLASS SHOW-OFF

YAH! THAT'S NOTHING. COME WITH ME!

MY DADDY WOULD LIKE ONE LIKE THAT...

CHUFFED

...TO USE AS BAIT FOR THE SHARKS HE CATCHES!

HMPH! BIGGER AND BETTER AGAIN!

EVERYTHING I HAVE IS BIGGER AND BETTER THAN YOURS!

EH?

TOFF 3

SLAM!

TIME FOR ELEVENSES.

FATTY HAS EIGHTSES, NINESES AND TENSES, TOO!

BET YOU DON'T HAVE ANYTHING BIGGER AND BETTER AT GUZZLING THAN FATTY.

CHOMP! GUZZLE!

DO YOU THINK SO? LISTEN TO MY MYNAH.

"TO BE OR NOT TO BE, THAT IS THE QUESTION..."

HE KNOWS THE COMPLETE WORKS OF SHAKESPEARE!

MAKES YOU LOOK RATHER PATHETIC, DOESN'T HE? GIGGLE!

At Cringeworthy Towers—

DADDY BOUGHT ME THIS!

WOW!

CUTHBERT ALWAYS HAS TO HAVE SOMETHING BIGGER AND BETTER THAN US.

GLARE

LOOK WHAT I CAUGHT!

WOW! WHAT A WHOPPER!

SMART NEW CAR, EH?

I KNOW HOW IT COULD SAVE PETROL.

HOW?

PUT IT IN THE BACK OF THE ESTATE CAR DADDY USES FOR DRIVING ROUND OUR ESTATE!

MUT 5

Then—

EEK!

ERK!

SWOOP

TITTER! YES, I DO! DADDY USES THIS TO GATHER UP UNWANTED RUBBISH!

Next—

PRETTY BOY! PRETTY BOY

GREAT TALKER, MY BUDGIE.

HMM . . .

DON'T CALL ME PATHETIC!

BITE

COO! YOUR NOSE IS CERTAINLY BIGGER THAN OURS . . .

THROB

SWELL

. . . HOPE IT'S BETTER SOON! HAW-HAW!

Sydney can't come to school today because he's got...

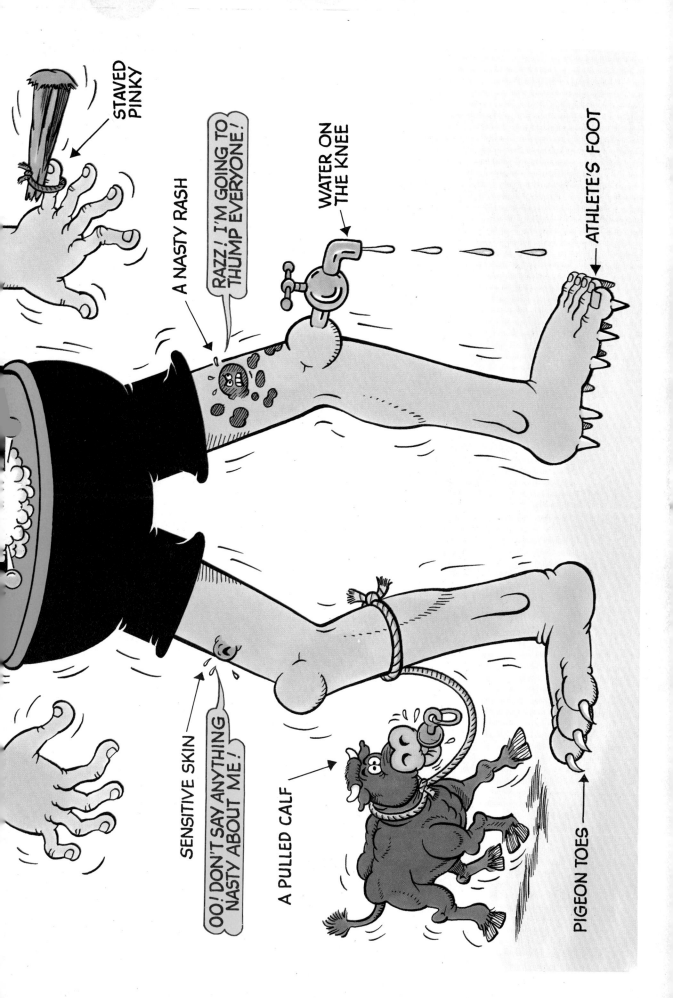

THAT SHRINKING FEELING

With the Bash Street Pups

HAVE A MICE DAY

JANITOR'S CAT

SKIP

NICE OF WINSTON TO LET US USE HIS TAIL AS A SKIPPING ROPE!

YOU'RE TOO SOFT WITH THESE MICE—YOU'VE GOT TO GET RID OF THEM!

I'M NEXT!

HUH! IF YOU WON'T GET RID OF THEM I'LL FIND SOME OTHER MOUSE SCARERS.

I WANT YOU PUPILS TO GET RID OF THE SCHOOL MICE.

WHY SHOULD WE?

ALL ABOUT CHEESE

TRINN!
TRINN!

INTERVAL—
I'M STARVIN'

SLURP! SLOO!

WHAT'S GOING ON?

SLURP! SLOO!

BAH! THEY'RE MAKING PEA SOUP!

MORE, PLEASE!

SLURP!

CAN WE HAVE SOME MACARONI AND CHEESE, PLEASE, OLIVE?

SAUSAGE AND RHUBARB

OLIVE

MACARONI AND CHEESE

SCHOOL DINNER-LADY

WHY, OF COURSE! GLAD YOU LIKE

That afternoon—

SORRY I'M LATE—I WAS PICKING UP MY HOLIDAY PHOTOS.

GIVE THEM HERE, PLUG!

HEH-HEH-HEH!

PHOTOS
PHOTOS

EEARGH! THAT FACE!

SQUEAK!

So—
RIGHT, YOU LOT—OUT . . .

. . . ER—IF YOU DON'T MIND, THAT IS.

SORRY, WE DO!

OH, THAT'S ALL RIGHT THEN.

NOW FOR OUR SNACKS.

GRR! WE'LL GET RID OF THEM!

BURP!

A VOLLEY FROM OUR PEASHOOTERS SHOULD SHIFT THEM!

PUFF!

PUFF!

BLAST

WE DON'T LIKE IT—WE'RE USING IT TO GET RID OF THE MICE!

CHEEK!

ONE TASTE OF OLIVE'S AWFUL COOKING AND THEY'LL BE OFF!

But—

YEUCH! CHEESE SAUCE!

SPLAT!

SPLAT!

SPLUDGE!

RIP!

RIP!

MY PLAN WORKED!

YAHOO! THE MICE HAVE GONE!

But—

WELL, I COULDN'T LEAVE THEM HOMELESS, COULD I?

BEYOND A JOKE

LET ME SEE YOUR JOTTER, DANNY.

OO-ER!

ERK! WHAT AWFUL HANDWRITING—IMPROVE IT AT ONCE!

WHY, YES—I'VE GOT LOTS—LOOK!

CUSTARD

OLIVE

WELL YOU SHOULDN'T HAVE MADE SO MUCH, SHOULD YOU?

SNORT!

HAR-HAR-HAR!

I'VE JUST WRITTEN AN ESSAY ABOUT THE GREAT ACHIEVEMENTS OF OUR ILLUSTRIOUS HEADMASTER.

OO! LET ME SEE IT!

THE HEAD

HEH-HEH! IT DOESN'T SEE ME!

GOT YOU!

HO-HO! THAT WAS A MODELLING-CLAY MOUSE! GOOD LAUGH, EH?

ERK! I'M STUCK!

Later—

WE'RE HOLDING A SCHOOL CONCERT...

...AND YOU'RE GOING TO BE THE COMEDIAN!

M-ME? I C-CAN'T GO ON TH- THE S- STAGE!

At the concert—

ER—EM—WHY DID THE CHICKEN HAVE A FLY IN ITS SOUP? ... NO—THAT'S NOT RIGHT!

A FEW COLLARS MORE

JUST THE JOB

TINKER, TAILOR, SOLDIER, SAILOR, RICH MAN, POOR MAN, BEGGAR MAN, THIEF...

THAT REMINDS ME—WE'RE GOING TO HAVE A CAREERS CONVENTION.

PONK!

PING!

Then—

R.A.F.

BE A GOOD SAVER

ZIP!

ZIP!

AN ABILITY TO DESIGN 'PLANES!

BOO-HOO! MY 'TACHE!

ZONK!

OO-AR! FARMING'S A FINE, HEALTHY LIFE—UP AT DAWN TO FEED THE PIGS.

HERE, PIGGY—EAT THIS.

OINK!

SCHOOL COOK'S CUSTARD AWFUL!

TSK! TSK! SHE SHOULD BRING IT TO ME.

I'LL TELL HER!

BUMP!

So—

WE'LL TAKE YOUR MONEY TO THE BANK MANAGER, GRAN!

OK!

RUMBLE!

GRANNY'S BED

OO-ER—IT'S RUNNING AWAY FROM US!

ZOOM!

ANOTHER FAILED DUMPLING!

SCHOOL COOK

OLIVE

BOING! BOING! BOING!

EH?

OO

CRUMP!

THE SMASH STREET KIDS

WHAT A HANDSOME THING I AM!

SHATTER!

WE'VE MADE HIM WEAR THAT MASK, SO IT COULDN'T HAVE BEEN HIM!

WELL, IT MUST HAVE BEEN ONE OF THOSE OTHER HORRORS, THEN!

CHEEK! EVEN IF WE PULLED OUR UGLIEST FACES, WE WOULDN'T BREAK MIRRORS!

WHO WROTE BEETHOVEN'S FIFTH SYMPHONY?

NOT SMIFFY EITHER!

ER-UM... ER-UM...

THIS SHOULD REALLY MAKE FATTY MAD!

LUNCH BOX

SPOTTY'S NOT THE CULPRIT!

SOAP

GAAH! TAKE IT AWAY!

Eventually—

IT'S NOT SID EITHER!

SNIP! SNIP!

URGH! SCISSORS!

IT'S NONE OF THE KIDS AFTER ALL. WHO CAN IT BE, THEN?

THIS YEAR'S MODELS

THESE EXAM PAPERS ARE EXCELLENT...

OH, DEAR!

FAINT FAINT FAINT

WHAT I WAS GOING TO SAY WAS YOUR EXAM PAPERS ARE EXCELLENT FOR MAKING PAPIER MACHE!

SQUELCH!

Soon—

TRY MAKING SOME MODEL ANIMALS.

CLUMP!

So—

WHAT ON EARTH'S THAT, DANNY?

AND WHAT HAS MY STAR PUPIL MADE?

CUTHBERT CRINGEWORTHY THE GENIUS SITS HERE YAH! SNOL!

A "STAR FISH"— HOW WONDROUS!

I KNOW WHAT YOU CAN MAKE— MODEL OF MY HANDSOME FACE!

Then—

THANK GOODNESS THAT'S OVER!

TR-RRING!

TRRINNG!

In the lunch hall—

BY GEORGE, THAT SEMOLINA'S BETTER THAN USUAL, OLIVE!

OLIVE, THE NOT VERY GOOD SCHOOL COOK

THWACK!

THAT'S NOT SEMOLINA— PAPIER MACHE! SOMEON TAKEN MY SEMOLI!

MMI THE SMELLING-SALTS AREN'T WORKING...

...I'LL HAVE TO USE SMELLING PEPPER INSTEAD!

SHAKE

AACHOO!

AACHOO!

AACHOO!

CARRIER PIGEON ", OF COURSE!

LIKE MY " TORTOISE-SHELL CAT "?

DON'T TELL ME— IT'S A " MAGPIE "!

OD IDEA, ACHER!

So—

SPLAT!

SPLAT!

SPLAT!

GLERK!

TUG

THERE—PERFECT!

Later—

I'M TAKING THE AFTERNOON OFF TO PLAY GOLF.

BUT WHO'LL TAKE YOUR CLASS?

HEH-HEH! I MADE A MODEL OF MYSELF USING OLIVE'S SEMOLINA—BETTER THAN ANY PAPIER MACHE!

FIXED GLARE

Jest of a Wave

SLURCH!

BLURGH!

EVEN THE SCHOOL MICE EAT OUT!

Christmas Eve—

YAHOO! LUNCH TIME!

SCHOOL CANTEEN

GASP! I CAN'T BELIEVE IT!

IT'S NOT THE FOOD WE LIKE, IT'S THE CHARMS OLIVE PUTS IN HER CHRISTMAS PUDDING.

HERE HE IS!

GIVE US THAT BACK!

NOT LIKELY...

...IT MAKES A SUPER BOWLING BALL.

BOWLING ALLEY

RUMBLE!

OO-ER!

NEVER MIND! I'LL GIVE YOU BACK ALL THE THINGS I'VE CONFISCATED OVER THE YEAR.

COO!

But—

EH? WHERE'S ALL THE STUFF?

CUSTARD

POTATOES

YOU DON'T GET ANY OF THESE THINGS BACK UNLESS YOU EAT THE GRUB, TOO.

CLUMP!

TO PROTECT READERS OF A NERVOUS NATURE, WE WON'T SHOW YOU THE KIDS EATING OLIVE'S GRUB.

↑
EDITOR'S VOICE

GET THE BEANO - OUT EVERY THURSDAY!